Testimonials by si
looking for hope a~~~ ~~~~~~~~~~~

MW00573040

The quotes are original and unique, truly inspirational!
Lisa G

Hope's quotes are so uplifting...they will make you smile, laugh and/or
change any hopeless thoughts!
Sherrie S

Poignant, whimsical, sometimes obvious in a "wish-I'd-thought-
of-that" way, Hope's quotes tend to spark me to reflect anew upon
otherwise ordinary thoughts.
Marcia B.

Hope's quotes are sometimes witty, sometimes poignant, sometimes
whimsical... and always giving of hope for those who might have lost
track of it. I recommend reading any one of them to provide a bit of
inspiration for your day.
Brenda Bernstein, author

Hope's quotes offer meaningful sayings appropriate for many occasions"
Lynne G. Educator

Passive knowledge vs. an active understanding.
Beth K, QuoteHope® FB follower

"Fool's gold" is worthless, (Hope's quotes) a nugget of "hope."
Patti T, QuoteHope® FB follower

The number seven, in a sense: it's endless in "direction."
Patricia S, QuoteHope® FB follower

Brightens the corner where you are.
Wanda H, QuoteHope® FB follower

Review by D.C. Buschmann, MA

Initially, I wasn't sure if a whole book could stand alone with quotes and prompts. I was wrong! Not far into Hope Atlas's My Upside-Down World, I began to feel the intrigue of allowing my thoughts to fly and land where they would after mentally ingesting each quote/prompt combination. What a brilliant way to work through life's issues! One day I might feel like exploring certain quotes and prompts in writing and other days simply read and reflect. There is no judgment, Hope reminds us more than once—a major theme throughout.

As I continued to turn pages, the energy of my directed thought process became as relaxed as a session with my former trusted therapist. In her sessions, she, too, gave me helpful writing assignments. So, I decided on the days I write my ideas to the prompts, I will need my trusty notebook or journal (electronic or actual) or my tape recorder.

Farther along, it occurred to me that recording my responses in the privacy of my own space, whether at home in the comfort of my writing chair, at the park, or at my favorite bistro, I could explore life and my own issues and save money in the process. While Hope makes clear in her preface that she is not a therapist, I could see how these exercises, nevertheless, could benefit everyone.

That journaling is therapeutic has been proven. The one-liners and the prompts are thoughtful, inspirational, and a springboard to cultivating the self-acceptance and self-advocacy required to heal us from life's traumas by teaching us to respect our own thoughts, ideas, and distinctive voices.

As a poet, I intend to revisit many of Hope's quotes and prompts and let them take me where they may. I envision many bookmarks and tiny post-it-notes in my copy's future, and that's as it should be.

my Upside umop-down world

Journaling Through Unique Quotes & Writing Prompts

Thoughts about life that will inspire you to look differently at yourself and your world.

Hope Atlas
a.k.a. QuoteHope®

My Upside-Down World
Copyright © 2020 Hope Atlas a.k.a. QuoteHope®
ISBN: 978-1-7345553-0-1

Published by
Hope Atlas
www.quotehope.com

No parts of this publication may be reproduced, stored in a retrieval system, or transmitted in any form or by any means, electronic, mechanical, photocopying, recording, or otherwise, without the prior written permission of the copyright owner.

This book is sold subject to the condition that it shall not, by way of trade or otherwise, be lent, resold, hired out, or otherwise circulated without the publisher's prior consent in any form of binding or cover other than that in which it is published and without a similar condition including this condition being imposed on the subsequent purchaser. Under no circumstances may any part of this book be photocopied for resale.

Interior design: Amie McCracken www.amiemccracken.com
Cover design: Jessica Bell jessicabelldesign.com
Cover images: Clifton Hatfield, Ipopba

This book is dedicated to my father-in-law, Harold Atlas, for his honesty, humor and confidence in me. He was a kindred soul whom I miss dearly.

Preface

Who am I? I am someone who has found writing my life preserver since I was 15. Writing gives me a voice. I have been writing quotes for 3 years and have accumulated about 400 of them.

I AM NOT A MENTAL HEALTH EXPERT AND I AM NOT PORTRAYING THIS JOURNAL QUOTE BOOK AS A THERAPU-ETIC SELF-HELP BOOK. I LOVE QUOTES AND WRITING AND WANT TO SHARE MY THOUGHTS WITH YOU. PERHAPS THIS QUOTE JOURNAL WILL GET YOU TO LOVE QUOTES OR WRITE THEM, TOO! AND LIKE ALL JOURNAL WRITING IT WILL MAKE YOU THINK.

Through writing this book, I have grown in ways I would have never imagined. It all started with *Dreams fly by waiting to be caught*. This was my very first quote, written three years ago. On that same day I wrote 15 more. Then I kept writing and writing.

I set up a Zazzle online quote store and a quote Facebook page. I had fun writing the quotes and sharing them with others. At some point I started to think about writing a quote book.

The longer I thought about it, the more I did nothing.

So I stopped thinking about it and started looking into what I had to do. That is where *There are many different ME's* came into play. Many people know me as a quiet, private, behind the scenes person. So, to write a book, in a sense I had to re-write myself! Somewhere lurking inside me, there was another "me" that I had not focused on.

With great effort and again not thinking but doing, I started writing with the intent to publish—which brings me to the last quote that is quite apropos to this book: *You cannot fail life; revisions are always accepted*. And thank goodness for this one! I cannot count (although my book designer and editor can!) how many changes I have made to this book.

Most importantly, though, I did catch one dream. I hope you can too.

Introduction

LOL - Laughing Over Lemons.

That sums up life in three letters.

Here is my LOL day...

One morning, about a month ago, my car wouldn't start; I had left the lights on the whole night before. Later that day, I realized that there weren't any eggs in the fridge, so I went to the 7-Eleven at 10 pm in the rain. I slipped and dropped the whole dozen. I turned around and drove back to the store, where the kind owner gave me a new carton. When I finally got home, two of the eggs were broken. I made scrambled eggs.

As someone who uses writing as the vehicle for understanding myself, I took the opportunity to write and reflect on my day. I quickly named this (despite the obvious scrambled eggs theme) my "laughing over lemons" day. I started to look at the positives. At least I had enough eggs for breakfast and the broken ones had only fallen in the foyer, not in the living room. Some money was wasted, but how about that nice owner? Telling this story to my friend, who was having her own hard day, made her laugh, so that "almost" made up for it. More important, I tried very hard that night to remember the saying "let the little things go!" I then remembered that I had had a disagreement earlier that day with a relative. It was a lot easier to deal with the broken eggs than my own stressful family.

I sure got a lot out of that one quote. And the same thing happened with others as my list of quotes grew. I realized that my quotes could be used for others, too, as prompts or "jumping off" points to facilitate journal writing.

And so this book came together... a compilation of 278 random thoughts about life in no particular order. Some are serious, some are humorous, and some are twisted – just like life!

Within these pages I also have journal entries that reflect my own opinions and my life experiences. I offer them to give you a glance into my world and how I have learned from my quotes. Your emotions, opinions and life experiences will be different, although of course you might find some connections! I invite you to write your own unique thoughts about the quotes that are meaningful to you. This is the beauty of life and journaling.

So, are you ready to learn about yourself? Dive on in. Nobody can change anyone else and sometimes circumstances can't be "fixed"; but learning about yourself can help you change. Journaling helps us stay focused on ourselves. Some days you might only be able to write a sentence, other days your pen – or computer keyboard – will keep going non-stop. Don't worry about spelling, grammar, or whether it makes sense.

This book is meant to be used over and over. You will see each quote differently as you have new experiences; you will therefore see yourself and your world differently. If you get stuck on an entry, ask yourself why. My hope is that you will learn to use writing as your voice and your teacher.

LAUGHING OVER LEMONS

This sums life up in 3 words! Everything in your day goes wrong: What do you do about it? Can you find a tiny ounce of humor in the wreckage?

MAKE YOUR MIND LESS CLUTTERED - TALK MORE.

Today, find someone you trust and pour out
whatever is clouding up your brain.

THERE ARE NOT ENOUGH EMOJIS FOR ALL MY FEELINGS.

Have some fun. Make up some more emojis.

Sometimes you just have to stop and find your head.

When was a recent time you needed to take a break?

LET YOUR CHILDREN WANDER AS LONG AS THEY HAVE A GPS PROGRAMMED TO HOME.

How can you give someone you care about the space to experience something new without you?

IT'S TOO LATE TO SLEEP.

Write your own quote for the day!

SOME DAYS FEELING GOOD MEANS NOT FEELING BAD.

Write about one of those "not the best days."
How did you manage to make it OK?

WHEN LIFE GETS OUT OF FOCUS, BUY A NEW PAIR OF GLASSES.

What in your life needs re-evaluating?

Darkness lets the sky rest so it can wake up bright and early.

Take some time to reflect today.

WHEN LIFE GETS ROCKY, LET OTHERS BE YOUR LIFE JACKET.

Whom can you lean on today?

WHEN LIFE IS OVERWHELMING, CUT YOUR FOOD INTO SMALLER PIECES.

What are some mini-tasks that you can do today?

YOU CAN'T FAIL LIFE. REVISIONS ARE ALWAYS ACCEPTED.

What is one thing you want to change in yourself? What steps can you take?

I MEASURE WILLPOWER BY THE NUMBER OF TIMES I SAY NO.

What are you working on? Eating less junk food? Saying no to that extra favor?

I often lose hope, but eventually it finds its way home.

What steps can you take to find hope again?

SOMETIMES LIFE IS LIKE READING A BOOK WITH SOME OF ITS PAGES MISSING.

We don't always understand why something in our life is occurring. What's an explanation that would empower you?

YOU CAN LIVE FOREVER IN A FANTASY WORLD OR MOVE OUT.

What are you pretending about your world?
What changes can you make so your real life
becomes a better place?

WAKE UP YOUR DREAMS - NUDGE THEM GENTLY.

Reflect on some dreams you might have put back
to sleep. What could you do to awaken them?

DON'T WALK AWAY FROM YOUR PROBLEMS - RUN TOWARDS SOLUTIONS.

What challenges in your life are you avoiding and what steps can you take to start overcoming them?

Make friends with reality.

A stranger online once called me "Mary Poppins" after reading one of my inspirational quotes. She seemed to imply I was floating somewhere above the clouds, untethered from reality.

My first instinct was to start listing all my realities: my friends who are sick, my mother who was not such a good role model, my own illnesses. As I started to list them, I got angrier and angrier.

Then I took a step back and realized this person might have been dealing with her own realities. And that I didn't need to defend or explain how hard my own reality is. I am a fighter by default, but I this was not a helpful fight to pick.

What's important to me is to stay grounded as much as possible in my own real world, not get lost in a fairytale illusion. That takes making a conscious decision to handle my own life and get help when I don't think I can handle things myself. I have started to accept that I can't do everything alone. I need people.

When I started to make friends with reality, I got some remarkable results. I

1. Found acceptance – and peace.
2. Became more emotionally available.
3. Suffered less.
4. Laughed more.
5. Wasted less time.
6. Improved my eating and sleeping habits.
7. Gained more energy.
8. Strengthened my relationships and support system.
9. Had resources to help others more.
10. Screamed less.

When I am able to give up looking for what was or what could be, I can focus on what makes life tolerable or even good for today.

I have come to understand that not everything is a fight to be fought. Sometimes I have to take off my boxing gloves and shake hands with reality.

What are you pretending about your world? What reality can you accept that would make your real life a better place?

Let go of anger or
you will find yourself
with an overnight
guest.

What emotions are hiding underneath your anger?

WHEN LIFE IS PAINFUL, DON'T YOU WISH YOU COULD GET A HEART MASSAGE?

What can be your "heart massage?" Calling a friend? Taking a bath? Listening to music?

CONTROL WHAT YOU CAN IN LIFE: BUY AN UMBRELLA.

In what areas in your life do you have the ability to make positive changes?

IF A DOOR DOESN'T OPEN, DON'T BREAK IT OPEN.

What can you do to move forward gently?

LOVE MAKES THE SUN SHINE BRIGHTER AND THE CLOUDS THUNDER LESS.

Connect with your love today. Do you notice that your day is less stressful?

Love will stay strong
if you watch out
for cracks.

What is something you can do or say today
to make sure the relationships in your life stay
strong tomorrow?

SOMETIMES LIFE IS A LITTLE LIKE STEPPING ON A TACK — ALL YOU CAN SAY IS OUCH.

Is there a situation in your life where you haven't acknowledged that it hurts? What if you admitted your hurt to yourself or someone else?

When you are obsessing over a thought, pop popcorn.

There I go again, obsessing about that upcoming medical test, or spinning with anxiety over dinner tomorrow with a certain family member. But then, from the kitchen comes the pop, pop popping sounds of popcorn. And suddenly I'm thinking about the popcorn – which is much more fun! It's nearly impossible for me to keep worrying when popcorn is popping.

One way I'm able to stop obsessing over a thought is to directly address it. Here are some ways I do that:

1. Tell someone.
2. Write about it —get it out onto paper.
3. Draw or paint a picture.
4. Write a song.
5. Write a poem.
6. Write a story.

But this often is not enough. That's when I need to pop popcorn. In other words, distract me. Here are some ideas that have worked for me, and they may be helpful for you, too. Let me know what you think!

1. Erase all my junk email. It's a great feeling to have it all done.

2. Watch episodes of oldies, such as *I Love Lucy*, or a cute sitcom like *The Middle*.
3. Watch *Catfish* on MTV or almost any "reality" TV show. My favorites for a good laugh are *Wife Swap* and *Love It or List It*.
4. Read BuzzFeed articles. They're fun and silly.

5. Scroll through the "My Life Is Average" (MLIA) page on Facebook. It's not active, but the old posts are great to read! You can even try to make up some of your own. Here's one of mine: "Today, I went to wash my hands and there was no soap — MLIA — My Life Is Average."
6. Browse Pinterest. You can follow people who post content you like. For example, I LOVE the comic strip Mafalda.
7. Start an online business. There are a lot of online marketplaces to sell goods, such as Etsy, Zazzle, Amazon, eBay, and many more. Many have zero start-up fees.
8. Find a recipe for dinner. How about making pizza or bread from scratch?
9. Write a cookbook for your friends/family or community.
10. Make up a new mixed drink or new type of smoothie/healthy drink.
11. Read jokes and riddles online. There is every imaginable type of joke out there. I like "who am I" riddles and *Reader's Digest*'s extensive humor collection.
12. Learn origami.
13. Buy this week's groceries online. You can check out all the different choices, and you don't have to stand in line!
14. Plan your next vacation — or plan a day trip. How about a farmer's market, craft show, or car show?
15. Research restaurants or local places to visit, such as parks, towns, or new areas of a city.
16. Register for a TripAdvisor profile (it's free) and create reviews of places you've been.
17. Take a survey you received in the mail or online. Just make sure it's from a legitimate source.
18. Set up something new in the house, such as Netflix or music on your TV. Or program your smartphone to control every gadget in your house!
19. Take a walk to the store instead of driving. Or walk around a quaint or trendy town nearby.
20. Find a lecture or one-day workshop on something that interests you. Local community centers or adult education schools are

good places to look.

21. Make doctor's appointments for all your check-ups from head to toe.
22. Go to a farm and then make a meal from what you picked.
23. Take care of things that need taking care of. Change the burnt-out light bulbs in your house. Or wash and vacuum the car.
24. Call someone you haven't spoken to in more than a year.
25. Buy a plant. Or maybe even a fish.

And when all else fails -I POP SOME POPCORN!

What thoughts have you been obsessing over? What can you do that will change your focus?

MAKE LIFE MORE MANAGEABLE — PICK A BOOK WITH SHORT STORIES.

Where in your life do you shoulder too many responsibilities? How can you take on more manageable, bite-sized pieces?

LISTEN TO ANOTHER'S PERCEPTION OF YOU.

What positive and negative feedback are you getting? How does it help or hurt you?

THINK LESS INTO TOMORROW OR BACK INTO YESTERDAY.

How can we stay focused in the present? What is one thing we can do today?

If you look up into the sky and can't see the stars, look tomorrow.

What challenges are you encountering? What are your coping tools? Can you believe that it's possible for things to be better tomorrow?

DREAMS FLY BY WAITING TO BE CAUGHT.

What are your dreams? Have you slowed down
enough to catch them?

OPINIONS ARE GOOD CONVERSATION STARTERS.

What are some ideas you can share that can start a dialogue with someone in your life?

Enjoy the feeling of having nothing to decide.

It took me 40+ years, but I finally learned that it is okay to relax and for one day make no decisions.

I tried it once. I had some downtime and decided to do... nothing. And I'll tell you a secret: I enjoyed it.

The definition of relaxation: "To relieve nervous tension. To seek rest or recreation."
- Merriam Webster

How hard could it possibly be just to relax? Well ... very.

I spent most of my life running in circles, and what I got was burned out. When I had nothing to do, I would imagine I had to do something. This mindset was not serving me.

When I finally started taking time to relax, I got a lot of benefits. I found that I

1. Had more patience with difficult people or situations.
2. Met more new people and tried more new experiences.
3. Listened better and remembered more.
4. Got more done.
5. Was more fun to be around.
6. Slept better
7. Ate healthier.
8. Got sick less often.
9. Laughed more.
10. Screamed a lot less.

What a gift... to enjoy the feeling of having nothing to decide.

Some decisions in life don't need to be addressed today or anytime soon. What decisions can you put aside to address another day?

MEDITATION CONNECTS YOU TO A WORLD YOU CANNOT SEE.

How do you put yourself in a different world in a healthy way? Meditation? Music? Writing? Drawing?

TO AGREE IS EASY.

What do you do when you don't agree with something/someone?

Every word you say has meaning.

Words are very powerful. What has someone said to you recently that was positive? Negative? How did you react?

STRENGTH IS LETTING OTHERS INTO OUR WORLD.

Who are you shutting out of your life?

GRIEF DOESN'T KNOW HOW TO TELL TIME.

Take some time to reflect on any sadness
lingering in your life.

EVERY SENTENCE YOU SAY CAN BE INTERPRETED DIFFERENTLY.

Do you misinterpret people or think you've been misinterpreted? What is a recent example? Maybe it's time to get a reality check.

WHEN YOU SCREAM, I ONLY HEAR SOUNDS.

Where are your communication challenges? How can you communicate more effectively?

Yesterday does not have to dance with me today.

What challenges have you had lately and how can you focus on what's true now?

DON'T MINIMIZE YOURSELF. SOMEONE MIGHT STEP ON YOU.

How do you put yourself down? How can you change this pattern?

WAVES MAKE SWIMMING HARDER.

What challenges are you having right now?
How are you coping? What can you do to take
care of yourself?

START WITH SIMPLE RECIPES – THE FOOD WILL COME OUT BETTER.

Start small! What are some goals that you feel are obtainable?

THERE ARE MANY THOUGHTS IN A SMILE.

When you find yourself smiling today, pay attention: What thoughts are coming to your mind?

A seashell is pretty, but don't forget a crab lived in it.

Can you accept that even the most beautiful situations come with the possibility of some sharp edges?

DREAMS, LIKE ORIGAMI, CAN BE FOLDED IN MANY DIFFERENT WAYS.

There's always more than one way to reach a goal. Can you think of at least 3 paths toward yours?

LIFE HAS MANY DIFFICULT JOURNEYS – LET LAUGHTER BE YOUR COMPANION.

What are some ways you can find enjoyment amidst your struggles?

YESTERDAY I HAD ALL DAY TO WORRY ABOUT TODAY - SO TODAY I CAN RELAX.

How have you tried to relax today? What worries can you put aside for now?

IF YOU WANT SOMEONE TO CARE ABOUT YOU, TELL THEM HOW TO CARE.

How can you best communicate your needs to the people who need to know?

Knitting untangles my
thoughts.

Is your life complicated? What is one simple
thing you can do?

SMILING WHEN YOU FEEL LIKE CRYING IS A LOT LIKE WALKING UPSIDE DOWN.

Do you pretend to feel ok?
What if you let your tears flow?

WET CLOTHES
EVENTUALLY DRY.

What issues have yet to be resolved?

A smile doesn't need to talk

Many years ago, I volunteered at an agency for adults with special needs. I will never forget Jamie. Her eyes shone turquoise, emanating a calming aura when she looked at you. She was tall and strong like a warrior. She delighted in hugs; they were the fuel for her infectious smiles. She communicated in sounds, some piercing like a microphone that's too close, some like the whimpering of a scared puppy. But most of all she laughed, as if everyone around her were making silly faces or perhaps telling a funny joke. Like a flower, she thrived when tended to. If you could smile, Jamie would like you.

I miss the pure innocence of her smiles. She taught me that A SMILE DOESN'T NEED WORDS.

Being with Jamie reminded me to enjoy the important things in life. There have been many studies that have shown smiling makes you happier. But don't just believe the studies—do your own experiment. See what happens when you live your life in quest of a smile. Maybe slow down to enjoy someone smiling and smile back in response. How about going out with someone you enjoy being with? When they smile, or when a stranger smiles, do you smile too? Try complimenting the stranger next to you on the bus and watch them smile. How does their smile make you feel? I bet you will smile again!

Smiling is a free and simple way to help yourself become calmer and happier. Be a detective and discover what makes you smile. A funny show, a funny book, cute pictures of animals or babies, being with your friends/family?

THE LIGHT FROM THE SUN, MOON AND STARS DOESN'T NEED TO BE PLUGGED IN.

Write your own quote!

SOMETIMES YOU JUST HAVE TO STEP IN THE PUDDLES.

What did you do recently even though it meant going out of your comfort zone?

When it starts
to rain, put on your
windshield wipers.

What are some strategies you can use to clear
a way through your challenges?

LIFE IS A LITTLE LIKE FALLING IN AND OUT OF LOVE.

What in your life used to excite you? Perhaps
there is something in your life that
you need to change? It's natural to lose
enthusiasm sometimes – now how can you
rekindle your joy?

Anxiety Is Like Trying to Recite the Alphabet Backwards

I know how hard panic is to endure. The familiar suddenly becomes completely overwhelming and simple things become impossible. The worst part is that during an attack, it is hard to think that it will ever end.

I want to offer one strategy I have used for myself to lessen my anxiety during an attack. I am not a therapist and am not recommending treatment. I only hope that one tool that has helped for me can work for you.

This practical technique is called Grounding.

Grounding has helped me stay rooted in the present and de-escalate an anxiety attack by bringing me back to the here and now.

At the beginning signs of panic, I pick ONE phrase from the list below, and keep breathing steadily. Inhale. Exhale.

(This is a big feat – but I try to choose from one of these.)

1. I am safe.
2. I know many people who care about me.
3. I will remember a favorite performance in my imagination.
4. I will remember a beautiful scene.
5. I will remind myself of all the things that I like to do.
6. I am okay.
7. This will only last a couple of minutes.
8. It always goes away.

"In the depth of winter, I finally learned that within me there lay an invincible summer."
— Albert Camus

My panic does not own me. Breathe, in and out... A,B,C... It is over.

What's ONE phrase you could pick from this list for the next time you experience anxiety? What difference might it make?

WHEN YOU ARE SURROUNDED BY DARKNESS, REMEMBER TO USE YOUR FLASHLIGHT.

What challenges are you facing and what are some coping tools you can use?

THERE ARE MANY DIFFERENT ME'S.

Most of us have different roles with different people. What are yours?

TO TRUST IS TO TELL THE TRUTH, EVEN WHEN YOU WANT TO LIE.

Whom do you trust?
What are you most afraid to say?

Grief doesn't know how to tell time.

Sitting under a tree reading a book, suddenly a memory appears. I choose to embrace the memory, hold it in my hand, turn it over and over, and ask... What is this memory telling me? A time together, a longing to share, a touch, a smell?

Is there grief in the memory?

I have learned there is no right or wrong place for grief to be. Grief can find itself anywhere.

Grief can make me smile and cry at the same time. It dissipates and then finds me again, perhaps in a day or a month, or sometimes in a year, suddenly resurfacing. I embrace it for the memories it holds.

How we look at our grief changes, but our grief never truly ends. Name a memory that has affected you today or recently.

My happy doesn't have to be the same as your happy.

What did I need to do to find my "happy?"

STOP LOOKING AT SOMEONE ELSE.

My best friend in second grade used to ask me, as we were walking to school together, "What's wrong?" And my predictable response was, "Nothing. I'm happy!" I would slap a smile on my face and figure I had just taken care of her question. Underneath, though, I wanted to know: Why can't I be "happy" like those people who don't have asthma, don't have a mentally ill mother , and don't struggle with depression?

My real life struggles sometimes made being happy impossible. It took me until adulthood to accept that not all aspects of my life had to be happy. Who said we have to be happy all the time? Happiness is not a given, and no one is always happy. For that matter, how do we determine what happiness means?

Well, let's look at this closely. If I win a million dollars am I now happy? Maybe for a few months, but after that, studies show the effects dwindle. If I am not depressed and I can get out of bed today, does that mean I'm happy? Maybe. To find MY happiness I have to go back to my new mantra, "My happy doesn't have to be the same as your happy." I finally understand that if I look at others to gauge my happiness, I will never be happy.

Happiness has never landed in my lap. It has taken conscious choice. What makes me happy? Connecting with my daughters. Enjoying a quiet dinner at home with my husband. Sitting and sipping tea with my mother-in-law. Getting a text message of "hi" from a family member or friend. Watching my fish swim. Seeing my plants flourish. Being a part of a spiritual community. Knitting a scarf. Helping out in a soup kitchen and conversing and laughing with the people who come to eat. Talking to an elderly women in a nursing home and seeing her smile. And, of course, writing and reading poetry and interacting with others who do as well.

So, what is YOUR happiness? What makes you (not your sister or the Mega Million Jackpot winner or the 2-year-old jumping on the couch) happy? What can you do to find happiness just for today? You will never find your own happiness if you keep looking for someone else's version.

Think about what adjustments in your thinking you must do to find YOUR happiness. Do you find yourself comparing yourself with others or pretending to be happy when you're not? What would it look like to truly "do you" and find your own authentic happiness?

Each tear you shed
has its own story.

What is your story?

THINK LESS ABOUT HOW TODAY WILL END AND MORE ABOUT HOW TOMORROW WILL START.

How can you plan for tomorrow?

IF YOU BUY A LOT OF
SHOES THEN YOU ARE
OBLIGATED TO FIND
PLACES TO WEAR THEM.

Where would you go? Have fun with this one!

BOOK SOME OF YOUR WORRIES FOR TOMORROW – THERE ARE STILL MANY OPENINGS.

Which worries can be put aside for tomorrow or even the day after?

TOMORROW IS TODAY UNLESS YOU MAKE DIFFERENT PLANS.

If you don't like today, what can you do right now to ensure tomorrow is different?

If I could weigh my inner strength, I would break the scale.

What challenges have you survived?

YELLING USES UP SPACE.

How can we resolve conflict in a healthier way?

WHEN LIFE GETS TWISTED, UNTANGLE EACH KNOT ONE AT A TIME.

What challenge can you unravel today?

THERE IS NO RIGHT OR WRONG PLACE FOR GRIEF TO BE.

Where is your grief today? When you heard a song? Saw a picture?

SOMETIMES DANCING WITH YESTERDAY WILL ONLY GET YOU DIZZY.

What part of yesterday don't you want today?

Before you start a sentence make sure you like the ending.

What is the last thing you said to someone that you hadn't thought through first? What would have been a better way to have approached it? Can you still fix it?

IF YOUR DAY IS NOT GOING YOUR WAY, WALK BACKWARDS.

Reflect on what this quote means to you.

THE DEFINITION OF BRAVERY: TURNING AROUND IF YOU GET LOST.

Where are you lost? What would it look like to find help?

SOMETIMES ALL YOU NEED IS FOR SOMEONE TO SIT NEXT TO YOU.

Who is that person or who might be someone you can reach out to?

HUGS ARE INSEPARABLE.

What—or who—brings you joy?

When you hit the
snooze button you can
go anywhere!

Have fun with this one! Where would you go?

LIFE IS SOMETIMES LIKE TIC-TAC-TOE: EVEN WHEN YOU WANT TO MAKE GOOD DECISIONS THEY ARE BLOCKED.

What obstacles have you encountered when trying to do the right thing?

UNDERSTAND YOUR TEARS, THEN YOU CAN START TO UNDERSTAND YOURSELF.

Take some time to reflect today.

AN APOLOGY MEANS SOMEONE HURT YOU.

What was a recent apology and did you accept it? What were the consequences of accepting/ not accepting the apology?

DEALING WITH YOUR EMOTIONS IS NOT A WASTE OF TIME — IGNORING THEM IS.

What emotions have you been avoiding and how can you start to address them?

Life without struggles
would be like life
without water.

What are some challenges that are motivating
you to change?

IF YOU JUDGE ME, I WILL JUDGE YOUR JUDGEMENT.

How do you make sure you are standing up for yourself?

I USED TO CARE ABOUT MY SIZE, NOW I CARE ABOUT ME.

Do you judge yourself? What changes in your thinking can you make?

RELATIONSHIPS ARE LIKE TREE BRANCHES - SOME KEEP GROWING, OTHERS ROT OFF.

What are some toxic relationships you have or had? How do you nourish the positive relationships?

SOMETIMES YOU NEED TO LET PEOPLE HELP YOU FIND YOUR WAY — NOT YOUR GPS

What areas in your life are you trying to navigate without help?

I am tired of trying
to be like everyone
else — I would love
to see everyone try to
be me.

How can you focus on yourself?

LIFE IS A LITTLE BIT LIKE BUYING A SHIRT — SOMETIMES IT TAKES A WHILE TO FIND SOME-THING THAT FITS.

Finding what we like to do, or whom we want
to be with takes time.
What is a recent positive new experience?

WHEN A NEGATIVE THOUGHT STARTS TO TALK TO YOU, TELL IT YOU ARE BUSY.

How are negative thoughts in your life affecting you? How can you change your negative thoughts to positive ones?

WHEN YOU TAKE A FANTASY AND ADD REALITY, YOU WILL FIND AN OBTAINABLE GOAL.

What is a dream you have and how can you make it a reality?

LOVE IS MAGIC
THAT STAYS.

What in your life is magical? A friend? A significant other? A child? A pet? A relative? A place? A piece of music?

It's easy to lie on the beach. The true test is being able to swim in the ocean.

Is there a risk you're avoiding? What would it look like to dive in?

DON'T LET ANYONE STOP YOU FROM BEING YOURSELF — OTHERWISE ONE DAY YOU WILL BE LOOKING AT A STRANGER.

Is there someone negatively impacting your life? How can you effectively communicate your needs and strengthen your relationships?

MAKE SURE YOU LIKE
WHAT YOU ARE SAYING –
ONE DAY SOMEONE ELSE
WILL BE REPEATING IT.

How have other people's words had a positive
or negative impact on you?

IF YOU SHAKE YOUR HEAD TOO MANY TIMES YOUR HEAD MIGHT FALL OFF.

WHEN LIFE GETS MESSY, BUY A MOP.

You don't have to lift weights to be strong.

Is it difficult for you to ask for help? Who can you reach out to today?

FRIENDSHIPS, LIKE GLASS, NEED TO BE POLISHED TO SHINE.

How do you support your friends?

BEHIND EVERY BAD DAY IS A GOOD DAY WAITING ITS TURN.

What challenges are you facing right now? What
better days are coming?

IF YOU STAND TOO FAR AWAY, EVERYTHING IS BLURRY.

How are you distancing yourself from life?

EACH TIME YOU SMILE, YOUR BRAIN SENDS ANOTHER HAPPY THOUGHT.

What would bring a smile to your face today?

Don't ask for watermelon unless you are ready to spit out the pits.

What is something in your life that you need to accept for all its character traits and aspects?

SOMETIMES YOU GET HONEY, OTHER TIMES YOU GET STUNG.

Life is bitter-sweet. What in your life is sweet?
Bitter? A combination of the two?

A THOUGHT BECOMES AN ACTION WHEN YOU GIVE IT PERMISSION TO JUMP.

What would it take to turn your insights into actions?

WRITING GIVES YOU A VOICE WITHOUT HAVING TO SPEAK.

How does writing help you
express your feelings?

GIVE THE WORD NO COURAGE TO STAND BY ITSELF.

When have you said "No," without feeling guilty?
Do you feel compelled to explain yourself?

If Life Were a Zebra There Would Be No Peacocks

I was a zebra once, but not anymore. Now I see life in full color.

In cognitive behavior therapy (CBT), all-or-nothing thinking means thinking in extremes. There is no middle ground: Either you're a success or a failure. This can make life harder than it needs to be.

Thankfully, through a lot of hard work, I was able to reduce my negative, all-or-nothing thinking and to start having more positive thoughts. I started to experience being a peacock.

Why be a peacock? Because living in extremes allows no room for growth or flexibility. There's only one option:

"The movie was terrible."
"I am stupid."
"I will never learn to play the piano."
"She's mean."

Here's the difference between the black-and-white thinking of a zebra and letting some color in:

ZEBRA: I will never learn a new language.

PEACOCK: I will find a beginner language class to see if I like it. (LIFE IS COLORFUL!)

ZEBRA: I hate talking to new people.

PEACOCK: Going with a friend makes it easier. (LIFE HAS BECOME COLORFUL!)

ZEBRA: I will never be able drive on the parkway.

PEACOCK: I will go to the mall with my friend so I have company while driving on the parkway. (THERE'S COLOR EVERYWHERE!)

ZEBRA: I am never happy.

PEACOCK: Going to the movies makes me happy so I will make plans to see one this weekend. (LIFE IS SO COLORFUL!)

ZEBRA: I have a terrible memory.

PEACOCK: I can't remember names, but I'm great at remembering how to get places. (COLOOOORRR!)

BE A PEACOCK AND SPREAD YOUR WINGS!

What are some of your Zebra thoughts? How can you turn them around and bring in a little color?

Don't let a single
snowflake turn into a
blizzard.

Is there anything currently in your life that you
need to watch so it doesn't get out of hand?

SOMETIMES STARTING OVER MEANS ERASING ALL YOUR BOOKMARKS.

What is happening in your life where you could use a fresh start?

Love Is When Separate Petals Come Together to Form a Beautiful Flower.

I think of my life as having petals that, when they come together, create a beautiful flower. Those petals are my family, friends, and teachers from all walks of life, that bring love into my life.

Flowers take care to stay beautiful. Otherwise they wilt and die. Relationships are the same way.

If I ignore others, my beautiful flower decreases in size. When I work at my relationships they bloom. I find it very satisfying to keep my relationships alive.

Here are my garden tips to keep relationships alive and blooming:

1. Start with good soil; a kind person
2. Mulch: pay attention to your relationships
3. Fertilize: keep your relationships rich and always learning
4. Remove wilting and dying leaves: take care to be around healthy relationships
5. Watch out for pests: Don't associate with negative people.

Who are the petals in your life that make you a beautiful flower? What can you do to sustain their growth?

Desperation is eating ice cream with a fork.

Have you ever tried eating ice cream with a fork? I have! It's not the easiest or the most perfect solution but it works in a pinch! It might seem like a ridiculous or "desperate" thing to do. But what's wrong with that when you have no other options?

Desperation | Definition by Merriam-Webster
1. loss of hope and surrender to despair 2. despair leading to rash behavior

NOTE – I am NOT suggesting a simple solution to abuse/ life-threatening situations, or severe mental/emotional situations.

In my life, I have felt alone and desperate for friendship. I have felt desperate to feel pleasure and happiness. I have a long history of having desperation immobilize me.

So using a fork to eat my ice cream is not such a terrible thing.

I have learned that the FEELING of DESPERATION does NOT have to lead to NEGATIVE ACTIONS.

I have learned that hopelessness can either immobilize me or MOBILIZE me.

"Desperation is the raw material of drastic change."
– William S. Burroughs

"Desperation is sometimes as powerful an inspirer as genius."
– Benjamin Disraeli

It IS possible to take positive actions in the face of desperation. And I know first-hand that what I am proposing is not easy. But when I have been able to take positive actions, I experience taking back control of the situation.

There is a cognitive behavioral therapy technique where you're encouraged to act OPPOSITE your emotion urge. I was desperate to have friends, so instead of acting on the feelings of hopelessness and then isolating, the idea was for me to make myself get out and meet people.

I hated the "volunteer, join a club" advice everyone gives. But then I decided if EVERYONE is giving similar advice maybe I needed to listen. So, I did some volunteering. This forced me to be around people and to talk to them. I did not make close friendships but I did make nice acquaintances that made my life feel less lonely.

I love to write so I decided to truly start writing more and submit my writing to journals. I could have given up and told myself I can't do anything. But I did the opposite.

> "Life begins on the other side of despair."
> – Jean-Paul Sartre

The opposite of desperation is hope. Hope is believing.

I invite you to read the following lines aloud:

When I find hope, life becomes easier.

When I find hope, I can help others who are having feelings of desperation.

When I give to others, I feel less desperate because I am not alone.

When I find hope, my desperate need to succeed turns to trust in myself.

When I trust myself, I can do anything.

When my life has felt desperate, and I don't have a spoon for my ice cream, eating it with a fork has given me some control. I could have said "forget it" and ended up angry: "My life is worthless; I don't even have a spoon for ice cream." I could have thrown the ice cream in the garbage!

But I didn't.

"If you're reading this...
Congratulations, you're alive.
If that's not something to smile about, then I don't
know what is."
– Chad Sugg, Monsters Under Your Head

What do you do when you're feeling desperate?
What's your default emotional urge and what
would the opposite be? Are you willing to try it?
What makes you smile?

HAPPINESS IS A GOAL, LOVE IS A DESIRE.

What do you need to do to enjoy today?

HOPE MAKES US VULNERABLE.

What is going on in your life that is uncertain?

MY PAST IS A PART OF ME BUT NOT WHO I AM.

A painful past cannot be erased but how are you making today and who you are different from your past?

Memories are like
a light bulb that is
flickering but hasn't
gone out.

What memories are affecting you today
positively and negatively?

I AM ALWAYS TRYING TO REACH FURTHER AND STILL KEEP MY BALANCE.

Do you overextend yourself? Do you need to slow down to keep from falling

I AM PICKING UP THE PIECES AND USING NEW GLUE.

Is there some part of your life that went wrong and you are now starting anew?

START EACH DAY WITHOUT ANY DEBT.

What can you do to complete each day and start with a clean slate in the morning?

CHAMELEONS MAKE CHANGE SEEM EASY.

Are you in the midst of change? It can be harder than it looks. What makes the changes worth it?

Don't judge me,
that's my job.

How can you become your own cheerleader?
Write down positive self-affirmations!

I CANNOT SEPARATE MY PAST FROM TODAY.

What parts of your past are creeping into today? How can you accept or change them?

WHEN YOU CRY YOU ARE LETTING GO OF PAINFUL MEMORIES.

What memories do you need to let go of?

CRYSTALS ARE SIMPLY ORDINARY SALT PUT IN THE RIGHT CONDITIONS TO TRANSFORM.

Put yourself in a situation that you will succeed.
What are some examples?

THE OPPOSITE OF ANGER
IS SELF-AWARENESS.

What can you learn from your anger?

Don't drive too fast –
you might miss
your turn.

How can you slow down and enjoy life more?

SOMETIMES WE HAVE TO IGNORE THE PEOPLE IN OUR LIVES WHO SING OUT OF TUNE.

How do you approach differing opinions of others?

OPEN UP YOUR BACKPACK AND TAKE OUT ALL THE OLD BOOKS.

What old patterns are weighing you down?

IF YOU NEED A MAGNIFYING GLASS TO FIND SOMETHING GOOD IN A PERSON (OR SITUATION) THEN MAYBE YOU NEED TO MOVE ON.

Is there someone (or something) in your life that you need to let go of?

LAUGHING BLOCKS ALL INCOMING, UNWANTED THOUGHTS.

Where's your sense of humor today?

If you compliment
someone you will
experience the power
of your words.

Give 5 compliments today. How did it affect
your experience of the day?

A UNIVERSAL LIFE GOAL: TRANSFORMING LONELINESS INTO ENJOYABLE ALONE TIME.

What can you do to enjoy time alone?

EACH TIME YOU SAY NO TO FEAR YOU ARE SAYING YES TO YOURSELF.

Fear doesn't have to stop you. Where can you take action even though you are afraid?

IF YOU DON'T KNOW WHERE TO DRIVE, ASK SIRI.

Do you have a goal without a direction? What resources can you tap into?

LEARN HOW TO SWIM: YOU'LL HAVE LESS CHANCE OF DROWNING.

What can you do today to help
your future success?

You still have
time to change your
storyline.

What in your life needs to change? How will
you accomplish this goal?

RELATIONSHIPS LIKE PLANTS NEED WATER TO SURVIVE.

How can you keep your relationships healthy?

WHEN YOU FIND LOVE, MAKE MULTIPLE COPIES.

What is your definition of love?

LIFE IS FULL OF WRINKLES. YOU DON'T NEED TO IRON THEM ALL OUT.

What is not in your control or doesn't need to be fixed right now?

WHEN YOU ARE HAVING A HARD DAY, PUT ON SOFT SOCKS.

What is your self-care on a stressful day?

If everyone is different, then everyone is special.

Instead of comparing yourself to others, write down some of your unique qualities.

IF I HAD A MAGIC WAND, I WOULD TURN EVERYONE INTO RABBITS.

Finish this sentence as many times as you'd like!

"If I had a magic wand, I would…"

TO STAY HAPPY, MAKE SURE YOU HAVE A BACK-UP PLAN.

Not all days are happy, how can you still get through them?

LAUGHING IS LOTS OF MINI SMILES.

Name all your smiles for a day.

SOMETIMES WE FALL GRACEFULLY
LIKE THE LEAVES IN A TREE,
OTHER TIMES
WE LAND HARD.

What are some coping strategies you have used?

Make life easier
tomorrow;
pay attention.

How can you make sure to stay in the present?

PATIENCE: RIDING A TRICYCLE EVEN IF YOU REALLY WANT TO RIDE A BIKE.

What goals are you working towards? Can you allow yourself to take baby steps?

PERSISTENCE IS WHEN
A PERSON'S DREAMS
ARE UNSTOPPABLE; EVEN
WHEN CONFRONTED
WITH A STOP SIGN.

What challenges are you encountering but
refuse to give up on?

SOME PEOPLE DON'T NEED A HEARING AID; THEY NEED A LISTENING AID.

Is there someone in your life that is not listening to you? How can you address this problem?

DON'T LET ANYONE INTERPRET YOUR DREAMS FOR YOU.

What dreams do you have and how can you accomplish them?

Sometimes I'm the cookie and sometimes I'm the cookie dough.

WHEN LIFE HITS YOU, PUT IT IN TIME-OUT.

What can you do for a self-care day?

LIFE IS LIKE JUMPING ON A BED; YOU MIGHT FALL OFF IF YOU ARE NOT CAREFUL.

Where might you be being reckless in your life?
How can you play safely?

IF YOUR DREAMS AREN'T COMING TRUE; MAYBE YOU NEED A NEW BED.

How can you create a satisfying environment?

IF YOU RUN FROM YOUR PROBLEMS YOU HAVE LESS ENERGY TO SOLVE THEM.

When did you last avoid an issue?

When stress turns your life upside down, hold on tight.

What in your life is stressful right now and how can make sure you are taking care of yourself?

NEGATIVE THOUGHTS ARE *SIMPLY THOUGHTS* IN A BAD MOOD.

Talk back to your negative thoughts.
What would you say?

IF I WERE AN EMOJI, WOULD YOU UNDERSTAND ME BETTER?

What do you want someone to know about you?

MAKE PANCAKES WHILE THE SKILLET IS HOT.

What does this quote mean to you?

MY HUGS HAVE MUSCLES.

If you are angry,
mash a potato.

How can you express your emotions in a safe,
productive way?

SOMETIMES FEELINGS SEEM LIKE THEY ARE SPEAKING A FOREIGN LANGUAGE.

Writing is one way to understand your feelings. What other ways can you find help understanding what you are feeling?

IF YOU JUDGE ME, I WILL JUDGE YOUR JUDGEMENT.

Do you feel that people judge you; is it justified? How can you stand up for yourself against criticism?

SAVE YOUR ENERGY - WORRY ONLY AN HOUR A DAY.

Try putting a timer on your negative thoughts.
How much more time will you have to be
productive?

MY THOUGHTS ARE MAKING ME DIZZY.

What are you obsessing over today?

Every bird sings a
song - you get to
choose the words.

What would the words be to the song of the
bird you are listening to?

THROW YOUR FRUSTRATIONS INTO A POT OF WATER AND WATCH IT BOIL.

Take some time to reflect on how you deal with frustration.

BE PATIENT WITH YOURSELF — YOU DESERVE EVERY SECOND.

What is a recent example of how you were not patient with yourself? What would patience look like?

DON'T RUN DOWN THE STAIRS - HOLD ONTO THE RAILING.

What is an example where you acted in haste?
What was the effect?

TELLING A SECRET DOES NOT MAKE IT GO AWAY.

Take some time to reflect today.

When you focus on yourself, others will begin to listen to you.

What are your interests and goals?
How can you achieve them?

THE LONGER YOU SPEND WITH CONFIDENT PEOPLE, THE MORE LIKELY YOU WILL CATCH WHAT THEY HAVE.

Do the people you know make you feel good about yourself? Do you need to re-evaluate who you spend time with?

WHEN WE STOP BEING STRONG, WE GROW THE MOST.

Do you ignore issues that need to be addressed?
What support systems do you need?

THE WORD FORGIVENESS IS A "MESSY" WORD.

What needs forgiving in your life? What are you avoiding? What steps do you need to take?

NEXT TIME YOU FEEL STUCK IN THE WEB OF LIFE, TAKE A LUNCH BREAK.

Write your own quote!

Before you speak,
make sure what you
say is what you want
to be remembered for.

What are some strategies you can try before
speaking to someone in in a negative way?
How can you prepare for these situations?

MY NATIVE LANGUAGE IS FEELINGS.

Feelings are universal. How can you help others
understand yours?

LOVE CAN BE MOLDED
INTO MANY DIFFERENT
FORMS. LET THE ARTIST
IN YOU CREATE BEAUTIFUL
PIECES OF ART.

How do you describe love?

YOU WILL NEVER BE HAPPY IF YOU DON'T KNOW YOUR DEFINITION OF HAPPY.

What does "happy" mean to you?
What do you need to do for yourself?

A SWAN IS BEAUTIFUL ONLY BECAUSE OF SOMEONE'S ARBITRARY DEFINITION OF BEAUTY.

What standards are you basing your well-being on? Are they realistic? Are they causing difficulties in your life? How can you alter these definitions to support you?

I'll give you
the benefit of the
doubt except when it
doesn't benefit me.

Take some time to reflect today.

YOUR SMILE MAKES MY EYES HAPPY.

Who in your life brings you positivity and joy?

A PERSON CAN BE INTELLIGENT BUT EMOTIONALLY IGNORANT.

What challenges are you experiencing with other people? What are some self-care strategies you can incorporate?

A CLOUDY DAY DOESN'T MEAN THE SUN HAS DISAPPEARED.

What can you do to remind yourself that a current challenging situation is temporary?

GRIEF HAS
NO BOUNDARIES.

Grief shows up anywhere and anytime.
Where is your grief today?

Life is like a potato pancake - sometimes you just have to shred it to pieces to put it back together.

What transformations have you experienced recently?

GO GREEN — WORRY LESS, SAVE ENERGY.

What would you do with all that extra energy?

HOPE IS BELIEVING EVEN WHEN YOU ARE NOT SURE WHY.

What do you believe in?

WHEN YOU SMILE, LIFE SEEMS A LITTLE LESS COMPLICATED.

What can you do today to smile?
What made you smile yesterday?

STOP THINKING SO MUCH, YOU ARE SMART ENOUGH!

Do you find yourself obsessing? What is currently causing anxiety? What can you do to relieve some of the anxiety and obsessive thinking?

Good friends have
long arms; they can
hold your hand no
matter where
they are.

Who is that special person that is there for you
no matter what or when? How can you remind
yourself that you have people who care about
you? (A friend, relative, therapist?)

A VASE ONLY NEEDS ONE FLOWER.

Who is that special person in your life?

SOMETIMES I WANT TO RUN AWAY BUT I KNOW I WOULD GET LOST.

What can you change to make your life better right where it is?

TELL YOURSELF YOU ARE IMPORTANT; THEN FIGURE OUT HOW.

What about yourself are your proud of?

IF YOU WAIT IN LINE,
EVENTUALLY IT WILL GET SHORTER.

What makes you impatient?

Acknowledgements

This has been an unexpectedly rewarding journey that I could not have seen to the end without the support of so many. Thank you first and foremost to my husband, Glen, for having the confidence in me to pursue this book.

My thanks go to Bob for his never-ending support in all that I do. To my mother-in-law for letting me talk incessantly about this project. To my daughter Rebecca for her excitement, liking my quotes on Facebook, and supporting my online store through purchases and recommendations to others.

I am indebted to my daughter Sarah for supporting me throughout the writing process and for always cheering me on.

A huge thank you to my brother-in-law, Alan, for his help in editing my book. Thank you to Uncle Henry and Eva, Jeff and Debbie, my brother, Rob, and my extended family for their enthusiasm and support.

A special thank you to my friends, Marcia and Arnold, Barbara and Scott, Lisa and Dan, Lynne, Sherrie and Roger, Ilana, Andrea, Heather and Carly for their incredible enthusiasm, encouragement, feedback, and help. I am extremely grateful to my health and wellness professionals for being my cheerleaders and reminding me to take care of myself emotionally and physically throughout this process.

Huge gratitude to my book designer, Amie McCracken, for bringing *My Upside-Down World* to life with her artistic flair and her patience working with a new author. And a huge thank you to my dear friend and editor, Brenda Bernstein, for her meticulous editing, her creativity, and her ability to transform my prompts from the mundane to the intimate.

Last but not least, thank you to my Facebook followers for supporting my QuoteHope® page and to the wonderful people I have met on Twitter and LinkedIn.

About The Author

Since the age of fifteen, Hope has been putting pen to paper, writing her story through poetry, original quotes and memoirs. Writing is her life-line and her voice.

Holding a bachelor's degree in education from Cortland College and a master's degree in reading education from Syracuse University, Hope has worked for 31 years in literacy programs with children and adults. For many years, she also served as a bereavement volunteer, and most recently, she has been involved in community outreach programs.

Hope has a personal growth blog of quotes on *Medium Magazine*, a quote-focused Facebook page, and an online quote store. Her writing has been published in multiple online journals: *Anti-Heroin Chic, The Moon, Highland Park Poetry, Snapdragon: A Journal of Art & Healing, Intima: A Journal of Narrative Medicine, Hektoen International Journal, Wingless Dreamer, Down in the Dirt Magazine* and *Wolff Poetry Literary Magazine*.

When she is not up late writing, you might find Hope knitting her signature multi-colored scarves. She also enjoys Portuguese food, traveling around the world, and just about anything chocolate.

Visit my online QuoteHope® store at
www.zazzle.com/quotehope

Like me on my FB
facebook.com/QuoteHope

Follow me on Twitter
@quotehope1234

Follow me on my Medium Quote Blog
medium.com/@quotehope1234

See all that QuoteHope® has to offer at
www.quotehope.com

Made in the USA
Las Vegas, NV
08 October 2021

31857714R00132